Some other books by:

Kazuaki Iwasaki

スーパースペース	(Super Space)
宇宙と自然	(Space and Nature)
ほしへいこう	(Let's Go to the Stars)
魚の生活	(Life of Fish)
星の世界	(World of Stars)
科学の絵本	(Illustrated Science)
これが宇宙だ	(This is Cosmos)

Isaac Asimov

A Choice of Catastrophes
The Road to Infinity
Extraterrestrial Civilizations
Saturn and Beyond
The Collapsing Universe
Alpha Centauri, the Nearest Star
The Planet that Wasn't

Carl Sagan

Cosmos
Broca's Brain
The Dragons of Eden
The Cosmic Connection
Other Worlds
Intelligent Life in the Universe
  (with I.S. Shklovskii)
Communication with Extraterrestrial
  Intelligence (Editor)

VISIONS OF THE UNIVERSE

VISIONS OF THE UNIVERSE

Paintings by   KAZUAKI IWASAKI
Text by   ISAAC ASIMOV

Preface by   CARL SAGAN

The
COSMOS Store

a division of Carl Sagan Productions, Inc.

Copyright © 1981 by Carl Sagan Productions, Inc.

All rights reserved under International and Pan-American Conventions. Published
in the United States by The COSMOS Store, Montrose, California.

Library of Congress Catalog Card No.: 81-66426

Asimov, Isaac
    Visions of the universe.

Montrose, CA: COSMOS Store
8104   810310

ISBN 0-939540-01-0

Manufactured in Tokyo, Japan
9 8 7 6 5 4 3 2

To Chesley Bonestell, For Inspiration

PREFACE

by Carl Sagan

*I*n my boyhood I found myself fascinated with the idea of other worlds — distant planets with strange creatures and still stranger events. Why not? After all, the Earth was only one of nine planets and there were billions of stars in the Milky Way Galaxy. I read books on astronomy and a few science fiction novels. But somehow my sense of those other worlds remained blurred, muted. They never seemed to have a reality of their own. In my mind's eye they were just slightly more exotic versions of the Earth. There was some imaginative leap I was unable to make.

And then by chance, as a teenager — already dedicated to a career in planetary astronomy — I came upon a stunning book called *The Conquest of Space* (Viking Press, New York, 1949). It had an introduction by the rocket pioneer, Wernher von Braun and a text by a science writer I had already read and enjoyed, Willy Ley. But the glory of the book was the paintings by someone named Chesley Bonestell. Here, before the Earth had ever been photographed from space, were plausible and meticulous renditions of our planet from above. There were utterly unearthlike visions of airless, cratered Mercury, a Venus swept with yellow dust clouds, a Mars covered with vegetation, Saturn in the blue and cloudless sky of its distant satellite Titan. And there was a chilling representation of Manhattan island after an impact by a small asteroid. The paintings were plausible; Bonestell (could the name really be French for "good star"?) had evidently taken great care to get things right. At last, I thought, I knew what another world might really be like.

As time went on Bonestell's visions stayed with me. They helped me to think about what the planets were really like. When, in 1960, at the request of the journal *Science*, I prepared a summary article on new findings about the planet Venus, I included a copy of Bonestell's Cytherean desert as a representation of what we thought we knew. But in the last two or three decades, the pace of planetary exploration (and astronomy in general) has been breathtaking. Most of the artistic as well as scientific visions of those times have not survived to ours. We have learned much and — at least as far as the solar system is concerned — revised almost everything. Bonestell's paintings now hang in a place of honor at the National

Air and Space Museum of the Smithsonian Institution in Washington. But it is now time for new visions of the universe by a new generation of painters following in Bonestell's footsteps.

In September, 1980, in conjunction with the first overseas showing of our COSMOS television series, I was travelling in Japan with my colleagues Annie Druyan and Gentry Lee. Our hosts insisted that we meet a gifted painter, who is also a very serious amateur astronomer, named Kazuaki Iwasaki. So there, in a small waiting room in the Osaka airport, we were treated to a succession of visual and intellectual delights: Iwasaki showed us his work. Not only did they have the graphic acuity and meticulous care which mark the best Bonestells, but also Iwasaki's images were clearly informed by the latest scientific findings. I know of only half a dozen artists in the world — some of them worked with us on COSMOS — who are capable of this combination of talents. But Iwasaki's work was also graced with a characteristic Japanese temperament. Annie was the first to say it: Iwasaki's paintings are too important to be known only in Japan. This book represents our collective effort to bring Iwasaki's vision of the universe to a wider audience. We have been very fortunate in convincing Isaac Asimov — one of the premiere science popularizers of this or any other day — to write an accompanying text. Its clarity is characteristically Asimovian.

I have by now seen these paintings many times. But I cannot even glance at them without being stirred again to wonder. Here are the graceful and intricate magnetic field lines of the Sun, traced by arches of luminous starstuff; an exquisite glimpse of the Earth four billion years ago; a bloated volcanically active Moon filling the sky; two graceful manned spacecraft of a few decades in the future, pirouetting towards a landing on the red planet Mars; an astonishing view of Saturn seen from the north pole of its airless moon Rhea; a contact binary star, perhaps Beta Lyrae, with a foreground planet illuminated by the red glow of spiralling star matter. These are landscapes etched by gravity and time. This is, pretty closely, how the universe is.

By studying these paintings, by imagining that we have somehow, miraculously, been dropped into them, we improve our understanding of the universe and ourselves. Within these pages many adventures wait.

TABLE OF CONTENTS

INTRODUCTION

by Isaac Asimov

*A*ll facets of science are, to the appreciative mind, equally beautiful, but some facets are more equal than others.

Traditionally, the night sky, which has been the inspiration of astronomers from the earliest times, is serene, fascinating and utterly beautiful. That is true even without the aid of any optical instruments. The unaided eye suffices.

How beautiful, then, are the visions produced by instruments that make it possible to see the otherwise unseeable — ringed planets; striped planets; clouded planets; stars large and small and in colors and in groups and in vast spiral aggregations. Add to that the rockets and probes of this generation which have uncovered wonders we have been the *first* generation to see: active volcanoes erupting into airlessness; rings within rings within rings; satellites covered by a global glacier, intricately cracked; tiny satellites interestingly grooved; vast and turbulent storms, within whose gaping tornado funnel the entire Earth could be neatly dropped; crater patterns of wide variety.

And beyond all that lies the realm of imagination. Given what we now know, we can extrapolate further sights from viewpoints yet unattained.

Combine the latest astronomical findings with the imagination and skill of a gifted artist and you have the paintings of Kazuaki Iwasaki — a selection of which are presented in this volume and for which I am delighted to supply the text.

VISIONS OF THE UNIVERSE

Sunspot

*T*he Sun is not the center of the Universe for the Universe has no center. It is certainly, however, the center of our own family of worlds, the warming, light-bringing fire about which the planets we know, including Earth, circle.

Life is the gift of the Sun and could not exist (or have formed in the first place, perhaps) without it. To human beings, Sunrise is the occasion for the beginning of activity; and the winter solstice, when the noonday Sun no longer sinks from day to day but begins its rise again with the promise of spring to come, is an occasion for rejoicing.

To the unaided eyes, the Sun is a circle of brilliant light, too bright to look at, perfect, smooth, unchanging, seemingly eternal. And yet, when the Sun is dim and ruddy at Sunset, dark spots have occasionally been reported. The optical illusion imposed on a dazzled eye? No. For in 1611, the Italian scientist, Galileo, observed and recorded numerous dark spots and watched them as they moved smoothly about the face of the Sun, which was clearly rotating on its axis.

There is no mistake. We now know that the Sun is almost always spotted, the spottiness rising and falling in an eleven-year cycle, the spots tending to move from higher latitudes north and south toward the Solar equator. And, every few centuries, there are periods that last for decades that show hardly any spots.

The spots are not really dark; they are actually bright; but they are cooler than the rest of the Sun and look dark by comparison. They are large. The Earth could be dropped into a spot of average size.

Closeup views of Sunspots are not yet possible in reality, but in the world of the imagination we can see them as in the painting here included.

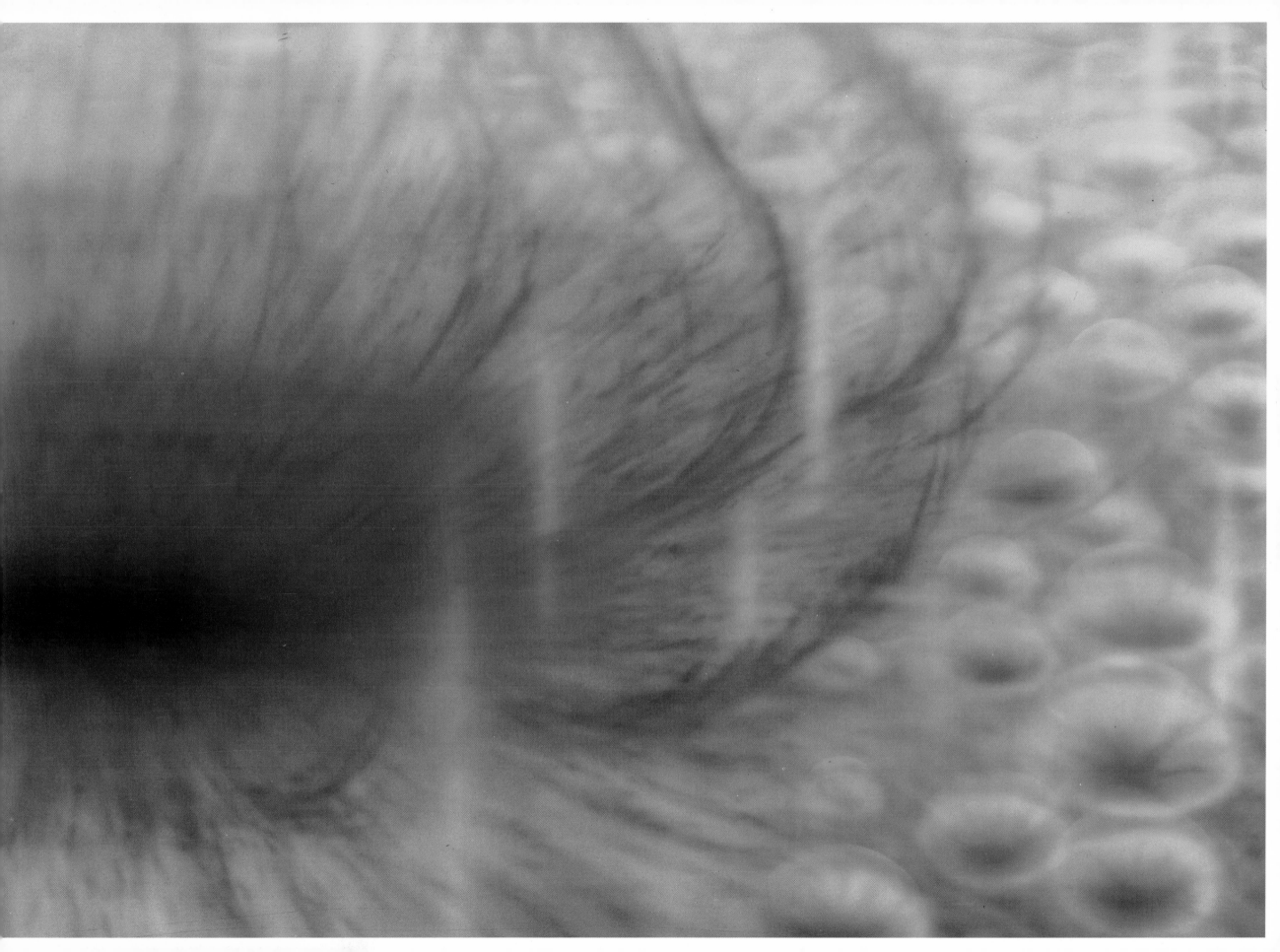

Sunspots and Prominences

S unspots are comparatively cool, it is true, with temperatures, at the center, of about 4,000°K., which is only two-thirds the temperature of the unspotted surface of the Sun, but that doesn't mean that the spots are comparatively mild and inactive.

Quite the reverse is true, for the spots are active regions of the Sun. There is much yet to be learned about the mechanism of spot formation, but it seems very likely that they are produced by unevenness in the Sun's vast magnetic field. The magnetic lines of force twist and loop as the Sun rotates, bellying upward from the Sun's interior past the surface. The plasma of the Sun (that is, the vast masses of charged atomic fragments produced by the Sun's great heat) swirls about the lines of force in a vast tornado-like pattern, so that the center cools and forms a spot.

The motion and the electromagnetic force, however, produce activities of all sorts. They produce explosions or "solar flares" which can occasionally be seen on Earth as small, even whiter spots against the Sun's whiteness.

Matter can also swirl up from the neighborhood of a spot like huge waterspouts except that in the place of water, we have spouts of red-hot gas. These can be seen at the rim of the Solar disc as red "prominences" that are particularly noticeable and beautiful at the time of a Solar eclipse.

In the painting we see the sprays of gases shooting upward. In the foreground is a prominence arching upward from a Sunspot, meeting another from a neighboring spot.

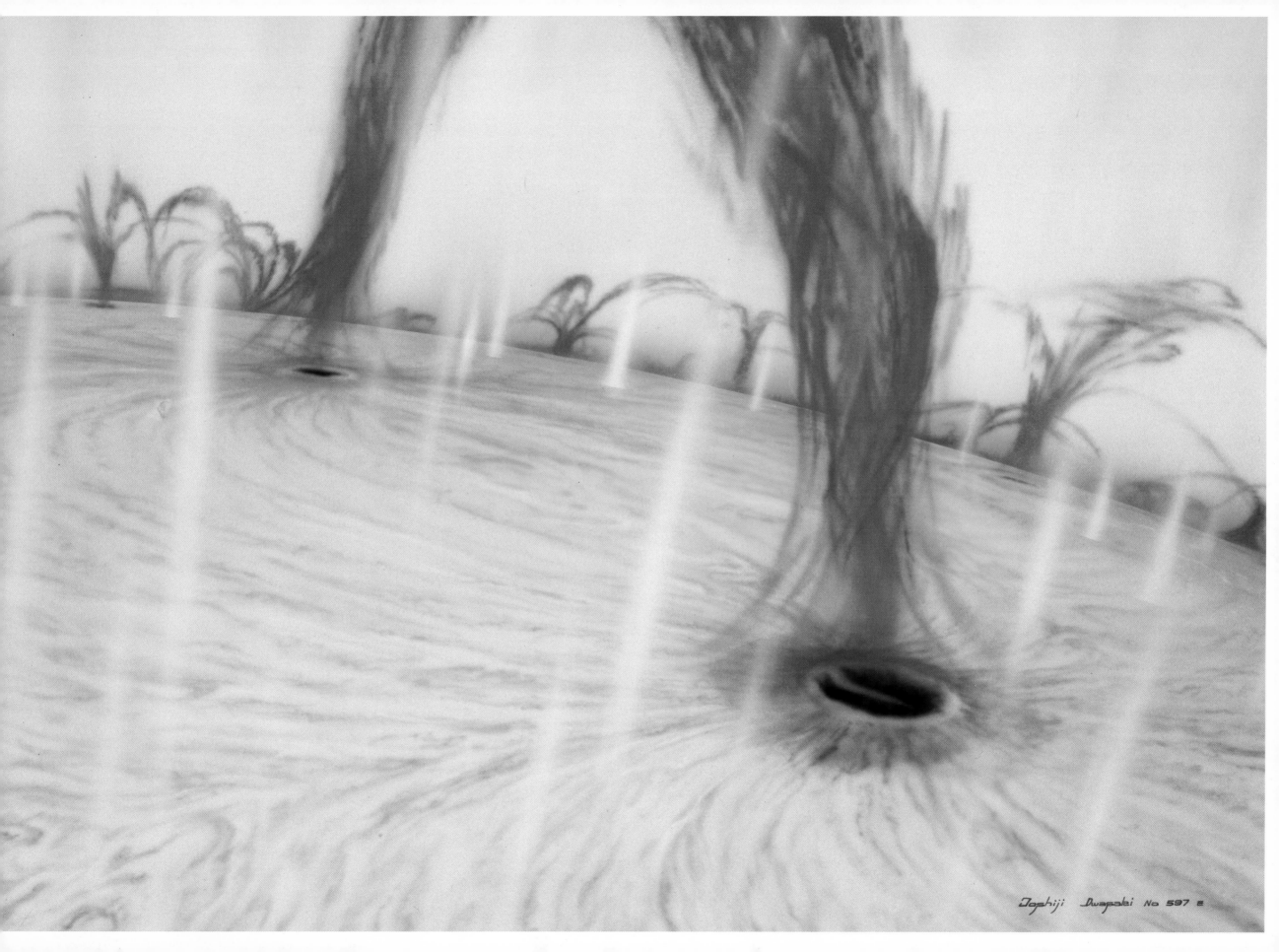

Toshiji Iwasaki No 597 e

Prominence

Prominences are not necessarily fired out of the regions about the Sunspots. They can also represent material condensing and descending out of the Sun's enormously extended atmosphere.

In doing so they can be, and usually are, diverted along the magnetic lines of force, sliding down such lines in a great arc toward a Sunspot. Since these lines may form a loop extending from one spot to its neighbor, the descending gases may do likewise and a vast arch of hot gas can form.

When such an arch happens to form over the edge of the Sun (as viewed from Earth) it shows up as one of the most impressive sights in astronomy, as you can see in the painting.

The prominences are about as hot as the ordinary surface of the Sun, 6,000 or 7,000°K.

Prominences were never seen until telescopes became available and even then they were not observed except during Solar eclipses when the blazing light of the Sun was obscured by the Moon. Prominences could then be seen to appear around the rim of the dark circle in the sky.

It seems odd to us now but astronomers were at first uncertain as to whether these gouts of red-hot gas belonged to the Sun or the Moon. It was not till 1860 that a British astronomer, Warren de la Rue, showed definitely that they were associated with the blaze of the Sun.

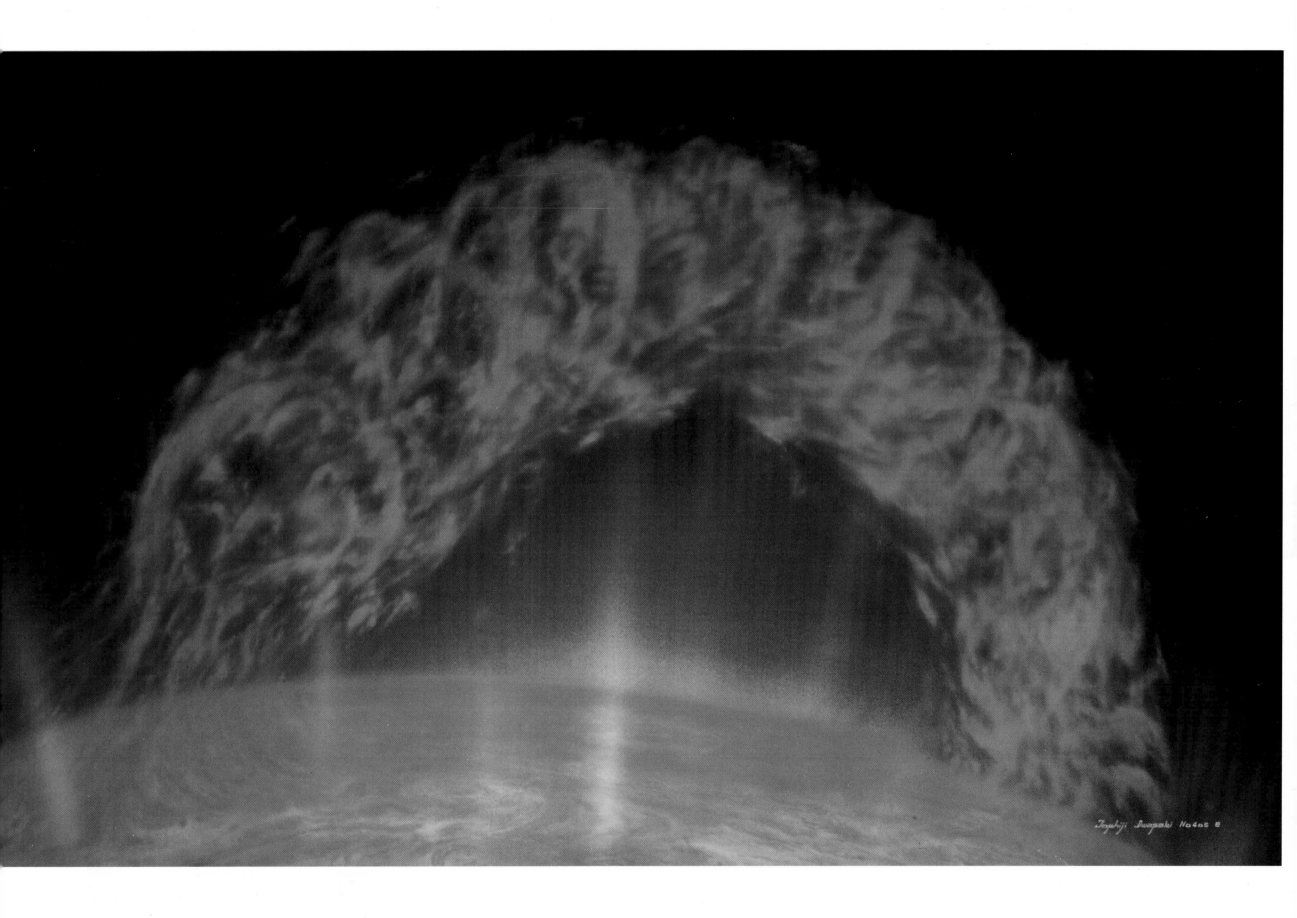

Ryohji Iwasaki No.405 E

The Sun

*I*n the first three paintings, the viewpoint was that of the neighborhood of the surface of the Sun. The first was closest to that surface, the second farther away, and the third still farther away. Now, in this fourth painting, we are far enough away to see the Sun as a whole.

There it is, the light and warmth of the Earth: benevolent patriarch that makes life and civilization possible on our planet.

It is a mighty monarch of the planetary system however. It is 1,400,000 kilometers across from side to side, which makes it 109 times as wide as the Earth. If the Sun were hollow, 1,300,000 bodies the size of the Earth could be dropped in to it and mashed down tightly before that hollow Sun could be filled.

Of course, the Sun isn't hollow and it couldn't be. It is a gigantic mass of gas that is 3/4 hydrogen and 1/4 helium (plus small traces of other elements.) Its temperature at the surface is about $5,800°K$. and at its center is about $15,000,000°K$. At that mighty core temperature, fusion reactions take place. Hydrogen nuclei (single protons) smash together to form helium nuclei, thus producing the energy that keeps the Sun radiating.

With that size and at that temperature, the Sun is a colossal giant. If it seems benevolent to us, it is only because its distance weakens the concentration of its energy output. It is 149,500,000 kilometers away from us and we would not want our world to be any closer.

In the painting, we can see Sunspots, and prominences, but all around we see the bright streamers of its upper atmosphere, the "corona", consisting of hot, streaming particles (temperature of 1,000,000 to $2,000,000°K$.). It is a vast halo about the Sun, thinning out into the "solar wind" that reaches to the planets.

Mercury

*W*e continue our voyage outward from the Sun and in our journey we will meet the planets, one by one.

The planet nearest the Sun is Mercury — waterless, airless, lifeless, baked in the Sun's heat as it slowly turns once every 59 Earth-days.

In 1974 and 1975, a probe, Mariner 10, took photographs of Mercury's surface at close range and revealed a world that looked much like our own Moon. The differences are, first, that it is larger than the Moon, being 4,850 kilometers across as compared with 3,476 kilometers for the Moon. (However, Mercury has only 3/8 the width of Earth and is only 1/18 as massive.) Another difference between Mercury and the Moon is that Mercury seems to lack the large "maria", which are areas of dark lava flows much larger than individual craters. Mercury, for the most part, seems to possess only the craters.

Of course, Mercury, which is at less than half the distance from the Sun that Earth and Moon are, has a sky that is dominated by the Sun. This is true more at some times than others. Mercury's orbit is quite elliptical so that it comes as close as 46,000,000 kilometers to the Sun at one point in its orbit, and recedes as far as 70,000,000 kilometers at the opposite point. Since it revolves about the Sun in 88 Earth-days, it reaches its nearest point (or "perihelion") every 88 Earth-days.

The painting shows Mercury at perihelion. The surface is Moon-like and crater-littered, and in the sky is the mighty Sun, with its Sunspot and prominences clearly visible (if there were any instrument that could withstand its heat and view it). Around it, following the lines of force of its magnetic field is its crowning glory, its beautiful corona all against the black sky that airlessness makes necessary.

Venus

---

*O*ur voyage away from the Sun continues. Venus is the second planet from the Sun, in order of increasing distance. It is a lonely planet, as Mercury is, for neither Venus nor Mercury has a satellite.

Venus, however, is much more nearly like Earth in size. It is Earth's twin-sister, being almost as large and with almost as high a surface gravity, and apparently with its bulk made up of very largely the same kind of metal and rock. What's more, Venus has an atmosphere as Earth has, and is covered by a cloud-layer even thicker than Earth's. In fact, Venus's cloud-layer is forever unbroken so that from Earth, we cannot see Venus's solid surface by ordinary light.

In past years, astronomers felt that the cloud-layer might keep Venus from getting too warm as a result of the nearby Sun. They thought the surface might be quite watery and that there might even be life on the planet.

Beginning in the 1950's, this was found to be a terrible mistake. Venus has an atmosphere that is 90 times thicker than ours and is mostly carbon dioxide. Carbon dioxide, along with other gases in the atmosphere, can hold heat, so Venus's surface temperature can be as high as 750°K., higher than that of Mercury. That temperature is maintained everywhere on Venus, day and night. The clouds contain water (although the surface is utterly dry at that temperature) but they also contain sulfuric acid, a corrosive chemical. Venus is certainly not a place where life as we know it can exist.

Venus's surface is largely flat, but there are at least two large, mountainous plateaus. The painting places us on one of these plateaus under the unbroken cloud-layer through which the Sunlight shines dimly. If Venus is Earth's twin-sister, it has somehow taken a wrong turning.

Kazuaki Iwasaki 1002

Volcanoes on Venus

We can't see the surface of Venus by ordinary light, but radar beams can penetrate the cloud-layer and reach the solid surface. There they can be reflected and the reflection can penetrate the cloud-layer again and reach us. By such reflected radar beams we can "see" the planet's surface, just as we might by reflected light. The vision is fuzzier by radar because radar waves are much longer than light-waves and therefore are not reflected as sharply.

From Earth, reflected radar beams don't show much detail. In 1979, however, a Venus-probe named "Pioneer Venus" mapped Venus by radar at close range. As a result we now have a better view of the surface than would have been thought possible a generation ago.

Some large and high mountains have been detected, which may or may not be volcanic in origin. We aren't sure. Venus's surface doesn't seem to be split up into plates as Earth's surface is. It is the slow movement of the plates against each other that produces earthquakes and volcanoes on Earth, and without such plate-movement on Venus these phenomena may be absent.

However, Venus, like Earth and all the planets, has a long history for it was formed about 4,600,000,000 years ago. In the past, it seems very likely that Venus was more "alive" than it is now, with a crust that was thinner and subject to greater activities. If there are no active volcanoes now, there may well have been many in the past. The painting shows an imaginative view of Venus's surface at a time when volcanic action existed and when the white light of the hot lava, spraying upward, enlivened and brightened the otherwise dull, cloud-covered scene in a way that made Venus still more hostile to life as we know it.

Kazuaki Iwasaki No. 860 EN

The Origin of the Earth

S till moving outward from the Sun as we go beyond Venus, we come to the third planet, our familiar Earth, our home and the only world we know intimately. Is there any painting of Earth that will not show us scenes we have seen innumerable times?

Ah, but we know Earth only in historic times — a duration of six thousand years which is but a moment in its mighty history. Can we picture Earth when it was first coming into being?

Five billion years ago, the region of space that was to become the Solar system was a vast cloud of slowly swirling dust and gas. For some reason (perhaps as a result of a pressure wave from a not-too-distant supernova explosion) the cloud began to condense under the pull of its own gravitational contraction.

It grew smaller, denser, more compact. Much of it condensed into a quite compact central core, but a few percent of the material remained on the outer fringes.

The larger dust particles grew at the expense of the smaller. Dust became pebbles; pebbles became rocks; rocks became boulders. On the outskirts of the cloud, bodies began to grow that were eventually to become planets whose gravitational attraction would sweep their orbits clear.

The central core, enormous in size, would develop increasing pressures and temperatures at the center till fusion would begin and the Sun would blaze into life.

As the planets formed, the colliding boulders would give up their energy of movement and the temperature would rise. Finally, the sphere of the Earth would take shape, glowing a dim red-hot as in the painting. The Sun in the distance is still hidden by its cloud and is only beginning to shine. This was 4,600,000,000 years ago.

Kazuaki Iwasaki 911.

The Infancy of the Earth

*E*arth experienced a turbulent infancy. Once its mass had come together, the heat it had collected from the gathering bits, whose collision and coming together had formed it, began to dissipate. The surface cooled and condensed so that a solid crust congealed about the planet.

While solid, it was still quite warm however, and comparatively soft and thin. Beneath it was still molten rock. Here and there where the activity below was greater than usual in the still-settling planet or where the crust was thinner than elsewhere, the molten rock would break through and well upward, or spray upward with varying degrees of violence. It was an incredibly violent period.

The surface of the Earth was too warm to support a water-ocean, so the planet was dry. However, geological and chemical changes would have released small molecules, small enough to be gaseous at Earth's temperature, so that an atmosphere would slowly form about the infant Earth. It would be a hot atmosphere subjected to the violence of the volcanoes from below and the heat and radiation from the young Sun above. It would collect electric charge and then discharge itself repeatedly so that the forming atmosphere would be in a perpetual state of lightning display.

Finally, although the Earth in its youth would have formed through the collection of the growing bits of matter in its orbit, it would take a long time before the last boulders in space were collected (some still exist today). Every once in a while there would be a new collision so that the Earth would be bombarded with meteoric strikes.

The painting shows the volcanic activity and the lightning of those days, and in the center is the oblique smash of a meteorite hitting its target.

Kazuaki Iwasaki 909 EN

The Earth's Ocean

*I*f the Earth was too warm to have an ocean in its infancy, where did the present ocean come from?

The original bits of matter that formed on the Earth included in their structure some of the lighter elements. There were water molecules, for instance, which were tied loosely to the silicate molecules that form the rocky layers of the Earth.

Most of this water was trapped in the deeper layers and could only slowly diffuse outward to the surface. By the time they did, Earth's growing structure had enough gravitational pull to hold the released gases to the surface as an atmosphere.

Some of the gases in the atmosphere were water vapor, and as the temperature of Earth's surface continued to drop, some of the water vapor condensed and rain fell on Earth's warm rocks and eventually collected in the deeper hollows.

Other water continued to work its way upward from the depths, so that the oceans grew more quickly than could be accounted for by rain. (Indeed, volcanic eruptions even today continue to spew water vapor into the atmosphere, among other materials. Much of this may be "juvenile water" that had never appeared on the surface before, so that the oceans may be growing very slowly even today.)

Eventually, though, very early in the game, Earth had its ocean, a portion of which is shown in the painting. Earth is unique in that respect. It is the only world we know of that has an ocean of liquid water.

The ocean as it exists today is a mighty body of water. It covers a total of 360,000,000 square kilometers of Earth's surface, or 70 percent of the whole. Its total volume is 1,250,000,000 cubic kilometers and its mass is about 1,350,000,000,000,000,000 metric tons.

The Earth Before Life

*E*ven after Earth settled down, it would by no means appear as the familiar world of today. The planet might no longer glow with heat, its atmosphere and ocean might have formed, but it would still seem a strange and hostile world.

For one thing it would be warmer than today and the ocean would have evaporated to a greater degree. There would be more water vapor in the air, and a thicker cloud layer. In fact, the early Earth, like Venus today, might well have been enveloped in a perpetual cloud cover.

Add to that the fact that volcanic activity, while subdued when compared with that of the still earlier period, would be greater than it is today so that added to the clouds of water droplets would be the gray drifts of volcanic dust high in the atmosphere.

As a result, Earth would be a gloomy place, dark and gray under its clouds and subject to frequent rainfall. The gray gloom is well shown in the painting.

What's more, Earth is as yet sterile and contains no life and you can see how far removed it is from the world of today.

Would astronauts from other worlds surveying the early Earth at this stage—its gray gloom; its unbreathable atmosphere; its unbearable warm humidity; the frequent earthquakes that shake its crust — would they guess that the Earth was still developing and would someday be our smiling, green, life-filled world?

Probably, for they would have had experience with worlds and they would know which were on the road to life and which were not.

Kazuaki Iwasaki 9/2

The Earth: Continued Development and Life

*E*arth never settled down to a dead halt. Even today it is geologically alive. Its crust exists in the form of a number of large plates, which slowly move relative to each other. Some plates pull slowly apart, allowing material to well up from below, widening an ocean. (This is called "sea-floor spreading.") In other places, plates come together and crumple to form mountains; or one slides under the other to form ocean deeps. At the junctions of the plates there are earthquakes and volcanic activity.

In the young Earth there was more of this than there is today. There would be places and times where volcanic action was very prominent, as shown in the painting, and there would be copious concentrations of energy available.

We are not yet certain as to the detailed chemical composition of the early atmosphere of the Earth. There is the possibility that it contained ammonia and methane, as in the atmosphere of Jupiter today — or nitrogen and carbon dioxide, as in the atmosphere of Venus today.

In either case, the small molecules of the atmosphere and ocean would, in the presence of energy, have come together to form larger molecules and still larger molecules. This would be a slow, random process but it would take place over all the vast ocean for a period of millions of years. The driving energy would come from volcanic activity and lightning if the earth were cloud covered; from the ultraviolet of the Sun, if the clouds had begun to break up as temperatures continued to fall.

In any event, when the Earth was much less than a billion years old, molecules had formed that were sufficiently complex to have the properties of life. Those molecules are our earliest ancestors.

The Earth and the Young Moon

*I*t may be that when the Earth formed, not all the material in Earth's orbit collected into the growing world. A small amount of it may have collected in a subsidiary nucleus to form a companion world, a smaller satellite of Earth. (The word "may" must be used here for astronomers are not yet certain that the Moon was a companion of Earth from the beginning. It may have formed elsewhere and been captured by the Earth — however, let us suppose it was formed in our neighborhood.)

The Moon is now quite a distance from the Earth and the action of its tidal effect, which is slowly forcing the Earth to rotate in a longer period, also acts to drive the Moon still farther from the Earth. In the past, therefore, it was closer to the Earth and in the long ago past, very much closer.

It may be, then, that when the cloud cover of the early Earth finally thinned and began to break and show portions of the sky, the biggest excitement (if there had been intelligent minds observing) would not be what we might expect. The sight of blue sky in place of gray clouds might be pleasing. The presence of bright light and the brilliant Sun in the daytime sky might be exciting. Yet more impressive than either of these might be the Moon—the young Moon—so close to Earth that it would appear five times as wide as it does now.

The painting shows what the view might look like. The lightning bolts and the meteorite strike show that the Earth is young, but there is the young Moon with its swollen body glowing in the sky. The Moon is itself still active. You can make out the glow of volcanic activity. It is too small to hold an atmosphere, however, so its outline is sharp (that's a full Moon in the painting, of course). You can see the craters of the larger meteorite impacts on the Moon, too.

The Last Days of the Earth

*H*aving spent so much time on Earth's infancy, it would be well if we took a quick glance forward in time to see how it will all come out.

Since the Sun and Earth have formed, 4,600,000,000 years ago, the Sun has been shining more or less steadily at the expense of the hydrogen fuel in its interior. Millions of metric tons of hydrogen are being converted into helium *every second* to maintain the Sun's steady radiation. However, so many metric tons of hydrogen exist that even after nearly five billion years only a fraction of it has been consumed and there is enough left to keep the Sun shining more or less as it is today for five to seven billion additional years.

However, as time progresses, the Sun's core grows richer in helium and denser; it contracts and grows hotter. Finally, five to seven billion years from now, the Sun's core will be so dense and hot that the helium nuclei will start combining to form still more complicated nuclei. By that time, the heat of the core will be great enough to cause the entire Sun to begin to expand.

The Sun will grow larger and larger and as it expands its surface layer will grow cooler. The Sun's fierce yellow will turn orange, then red. It will become a "red giant."

However, even though the surface will cool down and be at a lower temperature, there will be so much more surface that the total heat the Sun will radiate will be far more than it is today — and as it expands that surface will come closer to Earth.

The Earth will heat; the oceans will boil; the crust will crack. In the red inferno of the glow of the red-giant Sun, from which bits of glowing matter will rain down, as in the painting, the Earth will come to an end.

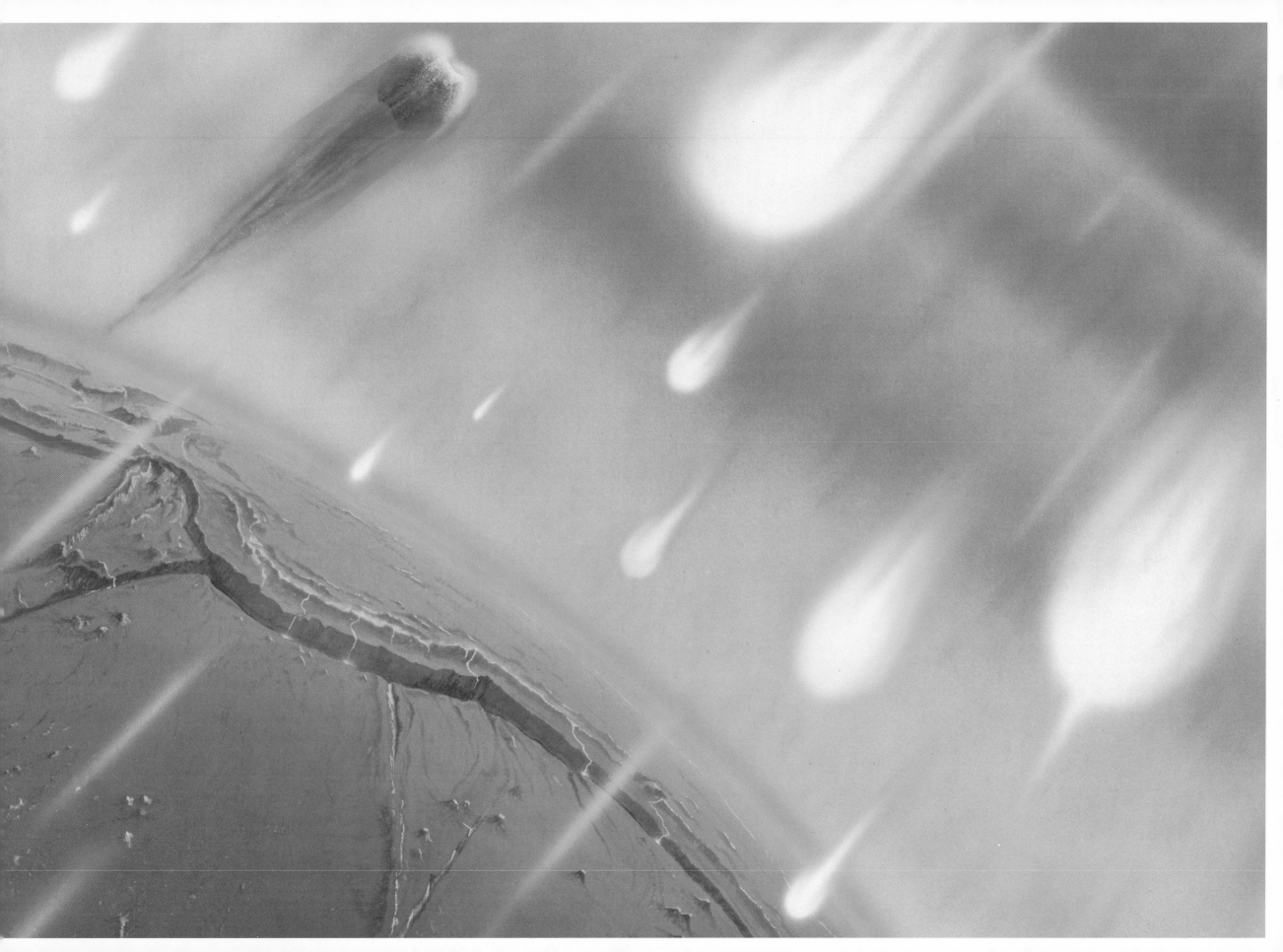

Skylab

L et us return to the Earth of today and begin to move away from it. In its near neighborhood are some objects that have never been present until the present generation: artificial devices of human origin.

The first artificial satellite was placed into orbit on October 4, 1957. In the quarter century since, many more objects have gone into orbit, serving a variety of purposes. Some have even served as primitive homes in space.

In 1973, the United States placed "Skylab" into orbit. It is shown here circling the Earth and passing over a portion of Earth's ocean with its light cloud cover.

Three sets of astronauts spent time in Skylab, up to three months of it. They could observe the Earth as no human beings could from its surface. They could observe the Sun, comets, stars, without any interference from an atmosphere. They could study the effects of zero gravity on human beings—themselves. And through it all they could live in comfort, amply supplied with food, water and air, with energy supplied by photovoltaic cells spread out on vanes to catch the Sunlight (even though one of the vanes was damaged during the launching.)

The Soviet Union has also put such objects into orbit and Soviet cosmonauts have on two occasions spent six successive months in space, and been supplied from Earth.

Skylab, after it had served its purpose as temporary home, continued to circle the Earth, unused, for five years. Unfortunately, its orbit slowly decayed and in 1979, after it had circled Earth 34,980 times, it finally penetrated the atmosphere, glowed red-hot and crashed to Earth. It had a mass of nearly 70 metric tons and there was some fear it might do damage, but it landed in the Indian Ocean and over western Australia. There was no harm to lives or property.

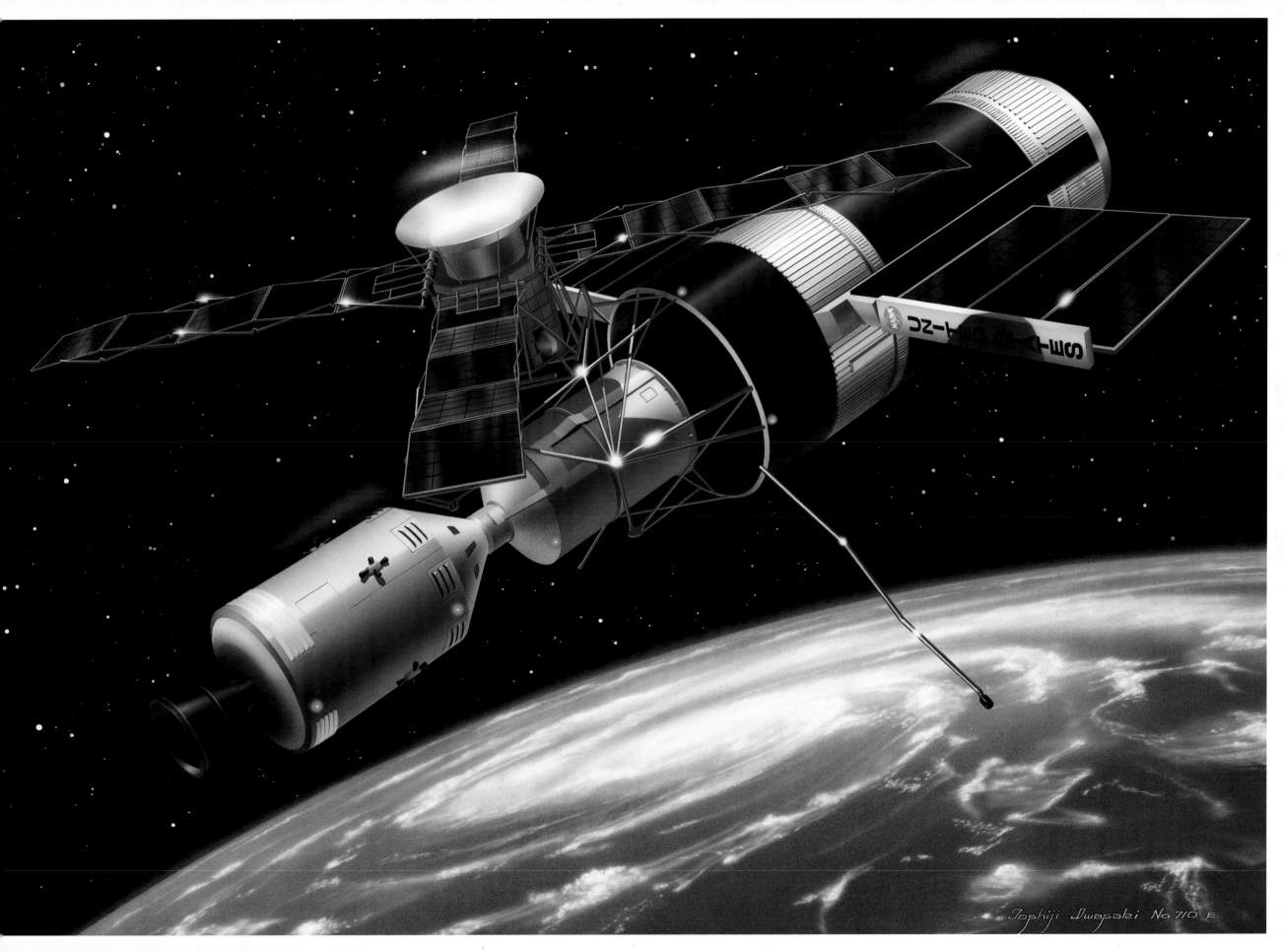

Toshiji Iwasaki No 710 E

Space Shuttle

*B*eyond Skylab is the Space Shuttle. Many years in preparation, it made its first actual flight in 1981. The Shuttle is a combination aircraft and spacecraft. It is piloted through air into space and then back into air. It is the first reusable spacecraft, and as its dolphin-like appearance noses through space in the vicinity of Earth, it holds the promise of a totally new era in space exploration.

Until now, Earth has been the base for all spaceflights and every vessel used for the purpose has been abandoned after one venture. This has made space exploration exceedingly expensive.

The Shuttle can go out and back, out and back, and the expense per single flight will plummet.

Furthermore, the Shuttle is designed to be the first space "truck". It can carry material out into space, and place it in orbit, then return for more material.

We have the picture then of a large space station being built, piece by piece, in orbit about the Earth; a space station that would be too large, too massive, too unwieldy to be launched from Earth in one piece.

In time, making use of the Shuttle (and of more sophisticated and efficient shuttles to be built with the experience and expertise that is gained of the first) we can build a variety of structures in space—solar power stations to capture energy from the Sun and beam it to Earth; observatories and laboratories; factories that make use of the properties of space for new ways of producing devices for the needs of humanity; even large space settlements that can house whole cities of human beings. The Shuttle is the key to a new space civilization.

Kazuaki . Iwasaki   No 810 E

The Earth From Afar Distance

*A*s we retreat from Earth, we can look back on the planet from a distance and see it as no human beings have seen it in all of history before.

To the ancients Earth seemed terribly small at first. They knew only their own patch of ground and imagined it to be a flat region over which the sky fit tightly, coming down to the ground all around. To travellers — soldiers, merchants, navigators — it seemed unaccountably large, for as they wandered they never seemed to come to the place where the sky met the Earth. It was only over the course of centuries that it was understood that the Earth was a sphere and that, though large, it had a definite size.

This is hard to believe, for even people who are taught in school that the Earth is a round ball suspended in space have trouble picturing it. But there it is. Artificial satellites and probes have taken photographs of Earth from space and sent them back to us. We then see what is shown in the painting — a blue and white sphere suspended in the blackness of space.

Naturally, we see only the Sunlit portion of Earth (as from Earth we see only the Sunlit portion of the Moon). In the painting most of the face of the Earth toward us is Sunlit, but in the lower right a portion of the face is in the night-shadow so we see not a full-Earth but a gibbous globe.

We see the dark ocean and the white cloud-cover, not unbroken as in the case of Venus. And we see bits of land—in this case eastern Siberia, Korea and Japan. (If they look strange it is because we see them with south uppermost. Turn the painting upside down and they will look more familiar.)

Earth Grazers

*N*ot all the small bodies of the Solar system went into the formation of the planets. Uncounted numbers remain circling the Sun to this day. Most of the larger ones are in the region between the orbits of Mars and Jupiter—the so-called "asteroid belt."

Some of these larger bodies, or asteroids, have orbits that carry them outside the belt. In 1898, an astronomer, Gustav Witt, discovered one he named Eros which strays into the region between the orbits of Mars and Earth and can come as close as 20,000,000 kilometers to Earth. This is closer than any of the planets, closer than any large object but the Moon. Since then we have discovered other asteroids which come even closer than 20,000,000 kilometers, now and then. These asteroids capable of a close approach are called Earth-grazers.

One of them, Hermes, detected in 1937, skimmed by us at a distance of only 800,000 kilometers. It was a small object, only a kilometer across, but if it had struck the Earth, it would have made a devastating impact. Some people think an asteroid 10 kilometers across struck the Earth 65,000,000 years ago and created such havoc that most living things died and many species, including the dinosaurs, became extinct.

There are Earth-grazers far smaller than Hermes which we don't detect and which are continually colliding with Earth. If they are large enough they land as meteorites; if they are smaller, they are just bright flashes ("shooting stars") in the sky.

As we retreat from Earth, we might pass a small asteroid hurtling past our home at (fortunately) a safe distance. You can see it in the painting outlined against the crescent Earth, irregular and rocky, capable of much damage if it struck, but passing us by safely this time.

The Moon

*A*s we recede from the Earth, we find that the nearest large astronomical body is the Moon, our constant companion in our steady journey about the Sun and, with the Sun, through the starry surroundings.

The Moon is very near us in an astronomical sense for its average distance from Earth is only 384,400 kilometers, only about 9.6 times the circumference of the Earth, and only about three days away by present-day spaceships.

What's more, it is a surprisingly large world. Its diameter is 3,476 kilometers, which is over a quarter of the diameter of the Earth. Its surface is as large as that of North and South America taken together. It has over 1/5 the mass of the planet, Mercury.

The Moon is not the largest satellite among the planets. There are five satellites that are larger — but not much larger. What's more, the other large satellites belong to giant planets far larger and more massive than the Earth. There is no other case in the planetary system of a planet as small as Earth having a satellite that is almost as large as Mercury. In fact, the Earth-Moon system can almost be called a "double planet."

The result is that the Moon is a magnificent sight in Earth's night sky—provided the sky is clear, of course—particularly when the Moon is full and near the horizon. Then it seems particularly large (which is an optical illusion) and may hang low in the sky like an orange balloon.

We can see it even more clearly through a small telescope or if we imagine ourselves closer as in the accompanying painting. Then we see the "maria" or large flat areas and the crater-flecked areas. You can see Tycho, the most recently-formed large crater, surrounded by rays of splashed material.

Crescent Moon

*A*s we move closer to the Moon, it looms larger and ever more impressively in our sight. It is not always a full Moon, of course. The Moon shines only by the reflected light of the Sun (as the Earth does, and all the planets and objects of the Solar system except for the Sun itself).

We don't always see the entire lighted hemisphere, for we see that only when the Moon is on the opposite side of the Earth from the Sun; when the Sun shines over Earth's shoulder, so to speak, and illuminates the entire Lunar disc that we see. Then we see the full Moon.

As the Moon revolves about the Earth, we see more and more of the Moon's night side—or at least we don't see it for it is too dark to see against the black night sky. The Sun-lit portion shrinks, until we see a "half-Moon" and then not even that. When the Moon is nearly between ourselves and the Sun, the side facing us is mostly in the night-shadow and we can only see a thin curving crescent at one edge (the edge facing the Sun) which is Sun-lit and visible.

We then see a crescent Moon.

This is true even if we are in a spaceship approaching the Moon. If we happen to be on the side of the Moon away from the Sun, we will see only a small portion of the Moon—but the crescent will be much larger than we see it from Earth.

We see a large crescent Moon in the painting as it would appear from an approaching spaceship — or from the Earth if a telescope is used.

At the boundary line (or "terminator") the craters are particularly noticeable, as the interiors are dark but the raised rims still catch the Sunlight.

The Surface of the Moon

*I*n 1969, American astronauts reached the surface of the Moon and human footsteps were formed in the soil of a world other than Earth for the first time.

It was a world far different from Earth, of course. To begin with, the Moon's surface is completely dry. There are no open bodies of water, and no water to be baked out of the surface rocks, either. There is no water at all and from the nature of the rocks, scientists suspect there was never any water. That means there is no life on the Moon, certainly not as we know it.

The dry land has its flattish areas but for the most part it is uneven and hilly as the painting shows. In its first few hundred millions of years of existence, the Moon was bombarded by the remaining bits of matter in space (out of which matter it had been formed). The craters (a small one is shown in the painting) are the marks of those hits and the strewn boulders have been thrown outward by the force of impact, especially by the larger crater in the lower right, of which we only see the edge.

Then, too, the Moon is an airless world. That means there are no air molecules and suspended dust to scatter short wavelengths of light and form a blue sky. The sky is black, even though the Sun is low on the horizon in the right. (You can't see the Sun but you can tell its position by the shadows.)

And, of course, if we are on the side of the Moon facing the Earth, the Earth shines in the sky, four times as large as the Moon seems to us from side to side, shining with seventy times the brilliance—blue and white, with occasional patches of light, its appearance changing, though it is always in the same spot in the sky. Undoubtedly, the most beautiful thing on the Moon is the Earth in the sky.

Kazuaki Iwasaki No. 848 e

The Visible Face of the Moon

*A*s the Moon revolves about the Earth in 27.32 days, it also turns on its axis in 27.32 days. That is not a coincidence. Earth's gravitational pull exerts a tidal effect on the Moon and that tends to slow the Moon's rotation which, when it was first formed, was undoubtedly much more rapid than it is now. When the Moon's rotation rate just matches its rate of revolution, the Moon is held in place by a "gravitational lock."

The most interesting effect of this equality between the rates of rotation and revolution is that the Moon always presents the same face to the Earth. Whenever we look at the Moon, we see the same pattern of shadows on its face. Whenever we look at it through a telescope, we see the same craters.

In the painting, we see this visible face of the Moon, the face we always see, in telescopic detail.

Notice that there are large flat areas almost free of craters. These are the "maria" from the Latin word for "seas." When the first people to use telescopes saw these flat areas (they are relatively dark and produce the faint smudges we see on the face of the full Moon) they thought they were actually seas.

This, however, is not so. You can see there are a scattering of craters on the maria and rays of ejected material from the newer large craters cross them.

Actually, the Moon is completely dry and the maria are places where molten rock from beneath the surface welled upward and spread outward, perhaps when some particularly powerful collision in the Moon's early days broke completely through the crust.

The Hidden Face of the Moon

*I*f one face of the Moon always faces toward Earth, the other face must always be turned away from the Earth and can never be seen if we see the Moon only from the Earth's surface.

Some people speak of the hidden face as the "dark side" but this is foolish nonsense. It gets the Sunlight just as much as the face we know; we merely don't see it. It is better to call it the "far side" or the "other side", or, as I do, the "hidden face."

Once people sent probes out into space, photographs could be taken of the hidden face and sent back to Earth. This happened for the first time in 1959 and a glimpse of something never before seen reached us. Eventually, probes were put into orbit around the Moon and then the hidden face could be photographed in detail and it was a hidden face no more. The entire surface of the Moon is now known even though from Earth only one face can be seen, as before.

The painting shows the hidden face of the Moon and it is different from the visible face in an interesting way. There are no marias, just craters. The hidden face seems to be evenly covered with craters, some large and some small, but there were no impacts that broke the crust and produced a large outspreading of molten material from below.

Scientists are not certain why this is so. Earth must have had some influence, but what?

By the way, how is it that all those chunks of matter hit the Moon and missed the Earth? Well, they didn't miss the Earth. The Earth in its early history must have been littered with craters, too. At least the land surface was. However, Earth had running water, and winds and living things, and all of these factors served to erode the craters and wear them down and eventually to erase any sign of their existence.

Mars

---

*B*ut now we leave the Earth-Moon system and continue on our journey away from the Sun.
Beyond the Earth is the planet Mars. It lies half again as far from the Sun as the Earth does. Mars' average distance from the Sun is 228,000,000 kilometers as compared with Earth's 150,000,000. It circles the Sun in 687 days, nearly two Earth-years.

Mars is distinctly reddish to the eye when viewed from Earth, which is why it was named for the bloody god of war. Through the telescope there is still a ruddiness about it interspersed with shadowy markings. In the painting, we see an imaginary spaceship on its way toward the planet which is pictured as it is seen from Earth.

In 1877 an Italian astronomer, Schiaparelli, reported seeing shadowy streaks on Mars which he thought might represent "canali", that is, narrow bodies of water, or, in English, "channels." The word was mistranslated into "canals" and a number of people felt that artificial waterways had been detected, which had been devised by a high civilization trying to maintain itself against a growing aridity. Mars was frequently pictured with a network of criss-crossing lines. They are not shown in this painting and it is well they are not for Mars-probes have shown that such canals do not exist. They were merely optical illusions.

Mars is a small world, only 6,800 kilometers across as compared with Earth's 12,750. Nevertheless, it resembles Earth more than the other planets do. It has a clear, thin atmosphere, with no cloud layer. Its axis is tipped as Earth's is, so that it has seasons as Earth does—but seasons that are colder and twice as long. It has ice-caps at the poles (you can see one on the left of the disc in the painting). In place of one large satellite, it has two small ones. You can see one of them on the lower right of the painting.

A Satellite of Mars

*A*s we approach Mars, we find that the planet is, in some ways, more Moonlike than Earthlike. Large portions of its surface are riddled with craters as the Moon is. This is not surprising, really. All the worlds of the Solar system were formed by the impact of smaller particles. Where worlds are small, waterless and airless, the marks of those impacts remain. Mars has an atmosphere but it is only 1/100 as dense as Earth's; it has water, but only small quantities, and mostly tied up as ice—so the craters are still numerous and clear.

Mars has two satellites: Phobos and Deimos. Deimos, the outer one, is 23,500 kilometers from Mars, only 1/16 as far from Mars as the Moon is from Earth. Phobos is even closer, for it is only 9,380 kilometers from the center of Mars and only 6,000 kilometers above its surface.

They are small irregular worlds, shaped something like potatoes. Deimos is only 16 kilometers across its longest diameter. Phobos is only 28 kilometers across. Deimos revolves about Mars in 30 hours; Phobos completes its revolution in 7 hours and 40 minutes.

Phobos actually turns about Mars faster than Mars rotates about its own axis, since Mars (like Earth) takes just about 24 hours to rotate. This means that Phobos, when viewed from the Martian surface, seems to rise in the west and set in the east.

In the painting we see Phobos at close quarters. Beyond it is Mars and its craters (but no canals). Phobos has its craters too, for it also must have suffered impacts. In fact, some of its craters are so large compared to its size that it may be that pieces were chipped off it.

Deimos, not shown in the painting, also has craters, but on Deimos, these are partly filled in by loose rock fragments. For that reason, Deimos looks smoother than Phobos.

Kazuaki Iwasaki No 765 EN

A Volcano on Mars

*I*n 1971, the Mars-probe, Mariner 9, reached Mars and went into orbit about it and, for the first time, the surface of another planet was thoroughly mapped. It turned out that the Martian surface had more than craters upon it. It had irregular markings that looked like dry river beds; it had an immensely long, wide and deep canyon; and it had volcanoes.

The largest of the volcanoes was actually visible from Earth but only as a light spot. It was called "Nix Olympica" ("the snow of Olympus"). In 1973, the name was changed to "Olympus Mons" ("Mount Olympus") named after the famous home of the gods in the Greek myths.

The Martian Mt. Olympus is far larger than the one in Greece, however. In fact, the Martian volcano is larger than any mountain on Earth. At its base, Mount Olympus is 400 kilometers wide so that if it were placed on Earth, it would stretch from New York to Washington, D.C. What's more, Mount Olympus rises 24 kilometers above its base, and that makes it far higher than any Earthly mountain. Mt. Everest is only 8.85 kilometers above sea-level.

In 1976, two human probes actually landed on Mars: Viking 1 and Viking 2. Photographs were taken of the Martian surface which was strewn with rocks and boulders, and the soil was tested for the possible presence of microscopic life-forms. The results didn't seem to give a clear answer. Some of the tests seemed to show that life might be present, but there seemed no trace of carbon compounds, which are indispensable to life as we know it.

Neither Viking landed anywhere near Mt. Olympus, however, and in the painting, we are shown what might have been seen if it had. The volcano (which doesn't seem to be active) towers upward toward its craters, the largest of which is 65 kilometers across.

Jupiter

*N*ow we travel outward from the Sun past the orbit of Mars and across the wide band within which numerous asteroids are to be found. In doing so we approach the orbit of Jupiter, the giant planet of the Solar system.

The diameter of Jupiter across its equator is no less than 142,900 kilometers, which makes it 11.2 times as wide as the Earth is. Its volume is 1,400 times that of the Earth.

Jupiter is not as dense as the Earth or as any of the inner worlds of the Solar system. Jupiter is made up of less dense materials than Earth is, because the giant planet has a gravitational field to match and can hold on to the light gases, hydrogen and helium, while Earth cannot. The result is that its overall density is only about one-quarter that of the Earth. Therefore although it takes up 1,400 times the volume that Earth does, Jupiter's mass is only 318.4 times that of the Earth.

Just the same, Jupiter's mass—the amount of matter it contains—is more than twice as great as all the mass of all the other planets, satellites, asteroids and comets *put together*. In fact, 70 percent of all the mass of the Solar system, outside the Sun itself, is found in Jupiter.

What we see when we look at Jupiter is the top of its cloud layer. From Earth, we see the cloud layer through the telescope as existing in bands of various shades of yellow, orange and brown, with a prominent "red spot." In 1973 and 1974, the first Jupiter-probes, Pioneer 10 and 11, passed the planet and gave us a closer look at the turbulent, twisting clouds, and at the giant vortex that makes up the Red Spot. The painting shows Jupiter as these probes saw it and one of the Pioneers is itself shown.

Toshiji Iwasaki   No 700 E

Jupiter and Io

*J*upiter is not merely a planet; it is a miniature Solar system in itself. Circling it are four large satellites: Io, Europa, Ganymede, and Callisto. Of these Europa is a bit smaller than the Moon, while Ganymede and Callisto are larger than the Moon. Io is just about the same size as the Moon. Ganymede, in fact, is 5,250 kilometers in diameter and is larger than Mercury.

Until just a few years ago, these four large satellites of Jupiter were just points in the sky to us. It was only when the Jupiter-probes began skimming by Jupiter that we could see them at close quarters. Ganymede and Callisto are icy worlds, each of them covered by many craters. Europa was a surprise, for it is covered by a smooth, satellite-girdling layer of ice, cracked in a complicated network. Europa looks very much the way people thought Mars might look, when they felt that Mars was covered by canals.

Io was an even greater surprise, for in some ways it was unique in the Solar system. It had been subjected to more heat than the other satellites, possibly because of Jupiter's tidal effect upon it. It was a dry world, strongly heated below, for it had volcanoes upon it. Unlike the volcanoes on Mars, those on Io were active. They could actually be seen in eruption, blowing gas and vapor into the airless space above Io's surface. Much of the material thus cast up is sulfur so that Io's surface is covered with yellow and orange sulfur-containing material.

In the painting we are on Io's sulfurous surface, with a volcano seen erupting on the horizon, and beyond it is Jupiter's monstrous orb. From Io, Jupiter is seen to have a width nearly 40 times that of the full Moon seen from Earth. The great storms can be seen writhing and swirling with the Red Spot just at the horizon.

Kazuaki Iwasaki 1000.

Jupiter and Amalthea

*I*o is the closest of the large satellites to Jupiter. It is 420,000 kilometers from the center of Jupiter, or more or less as far from Jupiter as the Moon is from the Earth. Of course, since Jupiter is so much larger from Earth, its appearance in the sky is much more impressive when seen from Io than Earth is when seen from the Moon.

Io is not, however, the closest of all the satellites to Jupiter. Inside Io's orbit is another satellite called Amalthea. Io and the other large satellites were discovered in 1610 with the very first telescope turned to the sky. It took nearly four hundred years and a much better telescope to discover Amalthea, which was first seen in 1892. In the first place, Amalthea is much smaller than the large satellites, only about 270 kilometers across its longest diameter, and therefore harder to see. It is especially hard to see because it is so close to the brilliant light of Jupiter.

Amalthea is only 181,300 kilometers from the center of Jupiter so that its orbit is only 110,000 kilometers above the top of Jupiter's cloud layer. At that distance, Jupiter's mighty gravitation has it in a firm grip so that Amalthea whirls around its orbit in only 12 hours.

Anyone standing on Amalthea would not care about anything but Jupiter. Amalthea faces one side always to Jupiter so that if you were on that side, Jupiter would always be in the sky. The circle of Jupiter would be over 90 times as wide as the full Moon is as seen from Earth; Jupiter as seen from Amalthea would fill up 8,500 times as much of the sky as the full Moon does.

In the painting we are standing on a portion of Amalthea's surface, from which Jupiter appears on the horizon. It stretches an eighth of the way about the horizon, always changing as it turns on its axis and as it goes through a complete change of phase every 10 hours. It is "full-Jupiter" in the painting.

Kazuaki Iwasaki   No. 862   EN 1010.

Jupiter's Red Spot

*T*he planet Jupiter doesn't resemble the Earth or its fellow-worlds of the inner Solar system at all. Earth has a metallic core, mostly iron, surrounded by a rocky mantle and crust. On top of the crust there are oceans and atmosphere. Venus and Mercury are much the same except that neither has an ocean, while Venus has a very thick atmosphere and Mercury has no atmosphere. Mars and the Moon have only a small core of metal, and Mars has a very thin atmosphere while the Moon has none; neither has an ocean.

Jupiter, however, seems to be a huge ball of mostly hydrogen and helium. If there is a core of metal and rock at the center it is comparatively small and, so far, we know nothing about it.

The outermost portion of Jupiter is a thick gaseous atmosphere of hydrogen and helium with some molecules of methane, ammonia, and water as impurities. In fact, the composition of Jupiter is much like that of the Sun. What's more, Jupiter gets hotter and hotter as one delves deeper into it, until it is at a temperature of tens of thousands of degrees C. at the core. Underneath the atmosphere is a vast "ocean" of white-hot, liquid hydrogen, and at the center is solid metallic hydrogen. However, Jupiter does not get quite hot enough at the center to start nuclear fusion so it does not become a star. It is an "almost-star".

The storms at the surface are tremendous. The Red Spot is a gigantic hurricane or tornado whose oval funnel at the top is 45,000 kilometers long and 13,000 kilometers wide. The whole Earth could be dropped into it without touching its sides. We don't know exactly what causes it, or what keeps it going for the centuries we've observed it or what gives it its color, but someday perhaps we'll find out. In the painting, we see it close up, an enormous red blister swirling about.

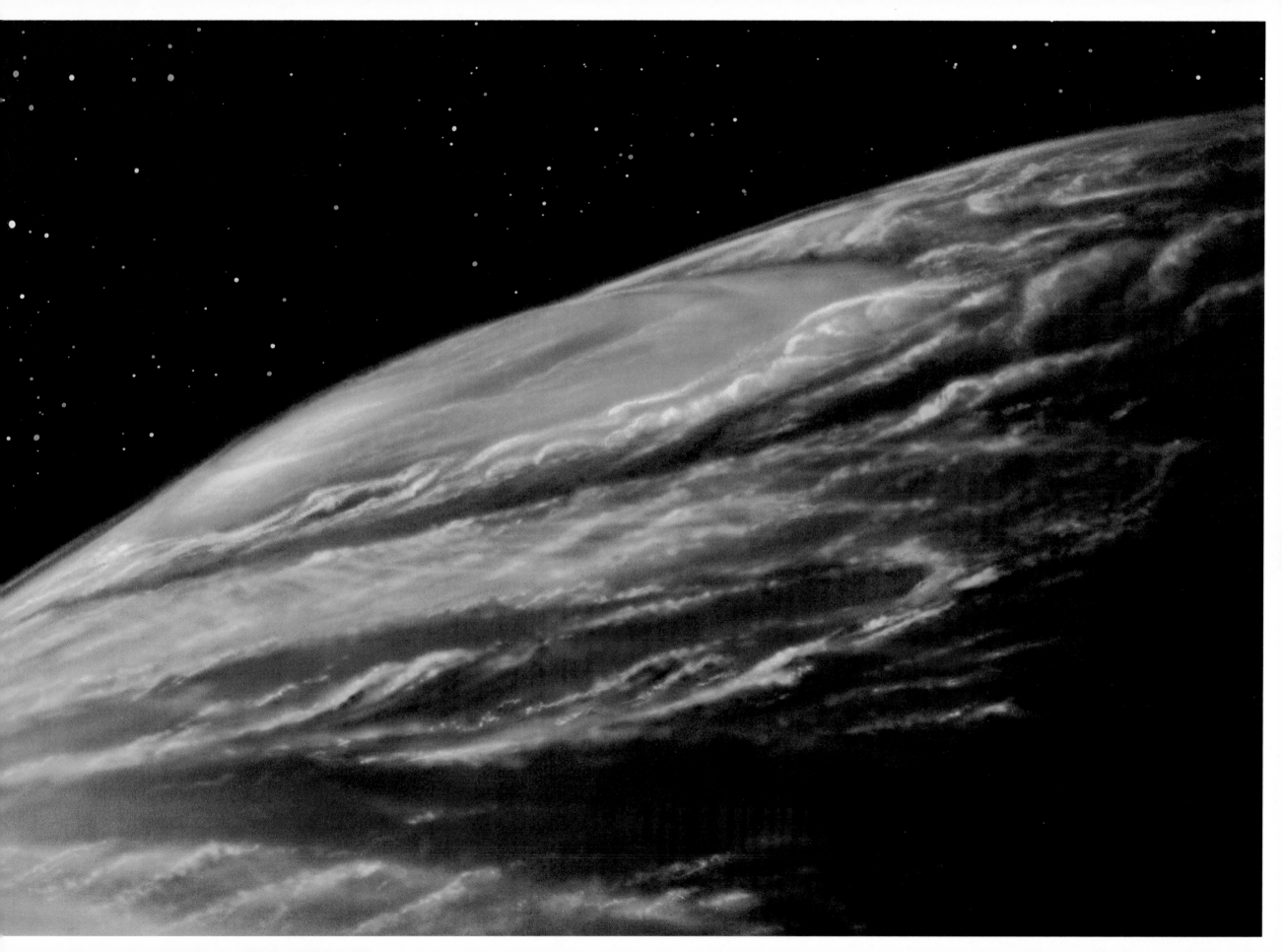

Saturn

*B*eyond Jupiter is that planet's small brother, Saturn.

Saturn is nearly twice as far from the Sun as Jupiter is. Whereas Jupiter is about 778,000,000 kilometers from the Sun, Saturn's distance is 1,430,000,000 kilometers. The intensity of Sunlight at Jupiter's distance from the Sun is only 3.7 percent that which reaches Earth; at Saturn's distance, the intensity of Sunlight is only 1.1 percent.

Saturn is smaller than Jupiter. Saturn's diameter at its equator is only 120,000 kilometers as compared to Jupiter's 143,000. Saturn's volume is only 3/5 that of Jupiter. Of course, that still leaves Saturn a giant as far as Earth is concerned. Saturn is 9.4 times as wide as Earth is and its volume is 830 times that of Earth.

Again, Saturn is made up of even lighter materials than Jupiter is. It must have a larger proportion of hydrogen to everything else; and it must also have a smaller core of rock and metal (if it has any such core at all). The material making up Jupiter has an average density 1.3 times that of ordinary water on Earth, but the average density of Saturn is only 0.7 times that of water.

The result is that Saturn has less mass than one would think a body of its size would have. It is only 95 times as massive as Earth even though it has such a huge volume. It has only 30 percent of the mass of Jupiter.

Both Jupiter and Saturn turn rapidly—about 10 hours per revolution. This flings their material outward in the equatorial regions so that neither Jupiter nor Saturn are really spheres. They are ellipsoids, fatter at the equator than from pole to pole. You can see that in the painting.

One thing, though, that Saturn has, no other planet has. Those are its large and beautiful rings, which show up dramatically in the painting.

Kazuaki Iwasaki 938

Saturn's Satellites

*L*ike Jupiter, Saturn has a large family of satellites. Where Jupiter has four large Moon-sized satellites, Saturn has only one, Titan. Titan is very unusual in having a dense atmosphere of nitrogen and methane. It is the only satellite we know of that has an atmosphere.

However, except for Jupiter's four large satellites, that planet has nothing but tiny asteroid-sized satellites circling itself. Saturn on the other hand, has nearly a dozen satellites of medium size, with diameters ranging from 300 to 1,600 kilometers.

There are at least half a dozen satellites that are closer to Saturn than Titan is. If one were to move inward toward Saturn from Titan, the next satellite one would come to would be Rhea. Whereas Titan is 1,222,000 kilometers from Saturn, Rhea is only 527,000 kilometers from Saturn. Rhea is a considerably smaller satellite. Titan is about 5,200 kilometers in diameter while Rhea is only 1,600 kilometers in diameter.

Nevertheless if we were interested in the view of the sky, it would be far better for us to be standing on Rhea than on Titan. On Titan the atmosphere would be smoggy enough to conceal the sky entirely (like the cloud layer on Venus). On airless Rhea, the sky would be unobstructed. Besides, think of the view of Saturn.

From Titan, Saturn would be seen to have 10.9 times the diameter of the Moon as seen from Earth; but from Rhea, Saturn would be 25 times the width and in the Sun's dim and distant light, it would shine 80 times as brightly as our Moon does. We would see the satellites that were still closer cross against its giant globe (as in the painting). We would not see much of the rings, though. At least we would see them edge-on and they would be too thin to make much show.

Saturn's Rings

*I*f we were standing at Rhea's north pole, we would see Saturn with its north on top, and its equator parallel to the horizon. That means that Saturn's rings would be parallel to its horizon, too, stretching across from left to right, as we see in the previous painting.

The rings are wide indeed; the visible portion (as seen from Earth) is 60,000 kilometers wide; but they are very thin. They are not more than 10 kilometers thick, so that they tend to disappear when viewed edge-on from Earth (this happens every 14 years).

From Rhea, which is much closer, the ring might not disappear altogether, but it would be a thin bright line and no more if it were viewed edge on. In this painting, we are pictured as standing on Rhea's equator and at a point on the equator in which Saturn is viewed on the horizon. It would stay on the horizon for Rhea faces one side always toward Saturn. What's more, we would then see Saturn with its axis parallel to the horizon. That means Saturn's equator would run up and down as seen from that point on Rhea and so would the rings.

Rhea does not turn precisely in the plane of Saturn's equator and rings. Its orbit is inclined by a third of a degree to Saturn's equator and therefore it is possible to move a little bit to one side or the other of the rings. Rhea takes 4 days and 12 hours to make a revolution around Saturn. This means that the rings seem to oscillate a little, moving first to the left and then to the right. It takes 2 days and 6 hours to move from left to right and then another 2 days and 6 hours to move back from right to left.

In the painting, we see the rings having shifted to the right and we can make them out in very foreshortened fashion. Notice, by the way, both in this painting and the one before, that the rings cast a shadow on Saturn's surface.

Kazuaki Iwasaki 761 EN

Within Saturn's Rings

When Saturn's rings were first discovered they were thought to be solid structures. The fact that they cast a shadow on Saturn's surface seemed to be proof of that. There was a dark circle separating two portions of the ring and some people even thought it was a dark coloring on a single solid ring.

However, a little over a hundred years ago, it was shown that the tidal effect of Saturn would break up a solid ring if one were there. The only way the rings could be stable would be if they were made up of myriads of separate particles that from a distance would seem to make up a solid ring—the way the bits of sand on the beach seem to make up a solid surface from a distance.

This is now accepted as certainly true. The Voyager I probe has shown that Saturn's rings are far more complex in structure than we had thought, since they consist of hundreds of subrings, some of them not perfectly circular, and some of them even seeming to twist in a braid. In the division between the two chief rings there is not total emptiness, but a few thin rings are located there, too. Astronomers are still trying to explain all these details—but the fundamental fact that the rings are made up of small particles remains.

In the painting, we are placed inside the ring. We see ourselves surrounded by boulders (we are not certain yet of what the average size is) which seem to be smaller and more thickly concentrated as we look off into the distance at the right until they fade into an apparently solid ring (seen edge-on as a white line) circling Saturn.

The material of the ring is so close to Saturn that the planet's tidal effects kept it from coalescing into a satellite. We now know there is similar debris in the neighborhood of Jupiter and Uranus, but only about Saturn is there so much that gorgeous rings visible from afar are formed.

Kazuaki Iwasaki No 790 EN

Saturn's Surface

*W*hen we look at Saturn's surface, what we are seeing is the top of Saturn's cloud-layers. In this respect Saturn is similar to Jupiter.

Jupiter, however, is larger and closer to the Sun. Jupiter receives more heat from the Sun and there is even some heat formed deep in Jupiter's interior, for it radiates away three times as much heat as it receives from the Sun.

This source of heat, inside and out, powers Jupiter's atmosphere and produces the vast storms and hurricanes that roil it so.

Naturally, since Saturn receives less than a third as much heat from the Sun as Jupiter does, and, being smaller, undoubtedly gets less heat from its own interior, there is less energy to set up storms in Saturn's atmosphere.

Therefore, Saturn is paler and quieter than Jupiter is. Nevertheless, it is not altogether quiet. It has its spots (white ones rather than red) that indicate storms and in the painting, we can see one whirlpool of gas marking a Saturnian hurricane. It seems small in the painting but it is undoubtedly some thousands of kilometers across.

And from Saturn's surface, looking up, we see something we can see on no other planet in the system—a broad system of rings arching from horizon to horizon. If we were on Saturn's equator, the rings would be represented only by a thin line, but we are pictured as well away from the equator so we can see it broad-wise.

The Sun is not visible in the painting, but if we were in the proper place on the surface and it were the proper time, the Sun would be seen winking through the rings. It would be a tiny ball of light, looking like not much more than a dot, now hidden, now momentarily visible. We would be in the shadow of the ring.

Uranus

*H*aving approached Saturn, moved down the line of its satellites, through its rings, past its surface— we now move beyond, still outward, past the limits of the Solar system as known to the ancients. Saturn was the farthest planet known to them and to the medieval astronomers and even to Galileo and Newton. It was not till 1781 that the astronomer, William Herschel, sighted Uranus and identified it as a new planet.

Uranus can just barely be seen by the unaided eye as a very dim star, but even a small telescope will show it nicely. It is twice as far from the Sun as Saturn is, for the distance of Uranus from the Sun is 2,870,000,000 kilometers. It takes Uranus 84 Earth-years to move about the distant Sun once. Compare this with the 29.5 years Saturn takes and 11.9 years that Jupiter takes.

Uranus is considerably smaller than either Jupiter or Saturn. Its diameter is 51,800 kilometers, but even so that is four times the width of the Earth. Its mass is only 1/22 that of Jupiter, but it is 14.5 times that of Earth. It is still a giant planet by Earthly standards, though compared to Jupiter it is a dwarf.

Uranus has five known satellites, but they are all middle-sized. The largest, Titania, is only 1,000 kilometers wide. Uranus is the only giant planet without a large satellite. In 1977, however, something far more startling was discovered. Uranus had rings, as Saturn did, but with a difference. Uranus's rings were far thinner, far darker, far dimmer. They couldn't be seen at all with even the best telescopes. What revealed them was the fact that they obscured a star briefly when Uranus passed in front of it. Voyager II will be passing near Uranus in 1986. The painting is a forecast of what it might see—the dim globe of Uranus surrounded by the halo of its dim rings.

Neptune

B eyond Uranus is Neptune. It was not discovered till 1846 and then through deliberate search, *not* by accident. Uranus did not quite follow the orbit that was calculated for it and astronomers thought there might be another planet beyond it whose gravitational pull was not being taken into account. The possible position of that planet was calculated by two different astronomers and when the sky was searched, it was found very close to the place that had been pin-pointed by the calculation.

Neptune, as it turned out, was almost the twin of Uranus. Its diameter is 49,500 kilometers, which is just a trifle less than that of Uranus. However, for some reason it seems to be denser than Uranus. We don't as yet know anything about the inner structure of either Uranus or Neptune, but it seems logical to suppose that the exterior is a large mass of light materials surrounding an inner core of rock and metal. The inner core must be considerably larger in Neptune than in Uranus. Because of this, Neptune has a larger mass than Uranus has. The mass of Neptune is 1.2 times that of Uranus and 17 times that of Earth---but still only 1/18 that of Jupiter and 1/6 that of Saturn.

Neptune is much farther from the Sun than Uranus is. Neptune is 4,500,000,000 kilometers from the Sun and it takes 165 years to move around the Sun once. Since Neptune's discovery, it has not yet made a complete circle about the Sun and returned to the spot where it was first sighted.

Neptune, unlike Uranus, has a large satellite. That is Triton, discovered only a few weeks after Neptune itself was. Triton is larger than the Moon, but smaller than Titan or Ganymede. It circles Neptune at a distance of 355,000 kilometers, just a little less than the distance of the Moon from Earth. If we were standing on Triton (as in the painting) we would see Neptune as a large circle in the sky; but despite the dimness of the distant Sun, Neptune is so much bigger than the Moon and so much better at reflecting sunlight that it would appear more brilliant than our own Moon does in the skies of Earth.

Pluto

*I*n the early part of the 1900's, astronomers were wondering if there might be still another planet beyond Neptune. It was not till 1930 that one was discovered and named Pluto after the Greek god of the underworld, because Pluto was so far from the light of the Sun.

Pluto's average distance from the Sun is 5,900,000,000 kilometers but its orbit is quite elliptical. At one end of its orbit it moves as far away as 7,400,000,000 kilometers from the Sun. At the other end, it is much closer: only 4,400,000,000 kilometers. This point of closest approach is the perihelion.

It takes Pluto 248 years to make one turn about its orbit so that since its discovery it has only had time to move 1/5 of the way around the Sun. Every 248 years, however, it approaches its perihelion and right now we happen to be living at such a time. Near its perihelion, Pluto approaches more closely to the Sun than Neptune does, and remains closer for twenty years. Right now it is closer to the Sun than Neptune is. It will reach the actual point of perihelion in 1989.

In the painting we are on the night-side of Pluto and we can only see a thin crescent illuminated by the very distant Sun. So far is the Sun that it appears in the sky as only a point of light, as just another star. Still, it is not quite just another star, for it is much brighter than any other. It is only about 1/2500 as bright as it seems to us on Earth, when Pluto is at its very farthest from the Sun—but even then it shines with 160 times as much light as our full Moon does.

The painting shows no detail about Pluto, because we don't know very much about it as yet. It was only in 1978 that astronomers discovered that Pluto has a satellite, which was named Charon. Once that discovery was made the size of Pluto could be calculated. Pluto is about 3,000 kilometers across (smaller than our Moon) and Charon about 1,200 kilometers across. They are small bodies.

The Orion Nebula

W ith Pluto we come to the end of the Solar system as we know it. There may be other planets beyond Pluto, but if so we have not discovered them yet. There are certainly comets whose orbits lie beyond that of Pluto in whole or in part, but we have never yet traced comets that far out.

Beyond Pluto all we have ever seen are stars and nebulae.

The nebulae are clouds of dust and gas, which do not shine of their own light. We can see them, sometimes, when they lie between us and clouds of bright stars. The "dark nebulae" obscure the light and stand out in silhouette.

There are some nebulae on the other hand that are huge, far larger than our entire Solar system. They include stars within their structure. Such nebulae glow in the light of the stars they contain and make beautiful sights in the telescope.

There is, for instance, the Orion Nebula, which is shown in the painting. It can just be made out with the unaided eye as the middle "star" of Orion's sword. In a small telescope it becomes a beautiful patch of glowing gas, a tiny luminous cloud in the sky.

It is a thousand light-years away (each light-year being a distance of 9,460,000,000,000 kilometers) and the light it glows with is lent it by a cluster of young and very hot stars, each of which is much more massive than our Sun. We cannot see these stars, for their light is diffused by the gas and dust of the nebula, just as the brilliant wire filament inside a frosted light-bulb cannot be seen because the frosting turns it into diffused light.

The hot gases immediately surrounding the stars are expanding and pushing against the cooler gases that lie at greater distances. This could force the cooler gases into contraction and lead to the birth of new stars.

Star Formation

*T*he dust and gas of a nebula are the raw material of star formation. Some stars may have come into existence near the time of the very beginning of the Universe, but most have been coming into existence during the billions of years that have elapsed since that beginning, and some are even coming into existence now.

A cloud of dust and gas holds together under its own gravitational field but that field may not be intense enough to force the dust and gas to collapse in upon itself. There may, however, be outside forces that push the dust and gas together to begin with. This will intensify the gravitational field and that intensification may be just enough to keep the cloud collapsing.

One outside force may be the vast explosion of a nearby star. A large star, when it explodes (as it does near the end of its life-cycle) is called a "supernova." The blast of the supernova may force the dust and gas together and start the cycle of contraction. Or else, if the cloud contains stars, the heat of those stars forces expansion of the gas near it and that pushes on the more distant gas and starts a cycle of collapse.

The Orion nebula is an example of the latter case and astronomers think they can actually detect objects that may be stars in the process of formation.

The clouds of dust and gas are turning slowly to begin with and, as they contract, the rate of turning speeds up. This is because the clouds contain "angular momentum" which must be conserved (stay the same in total). As the cloud contracts, the angular momentum decreases, unless the smaller size is made up for by a more rapid rotation. Therefore the condensing cloud turns more and more rapidly, so that the outskirts of the cloud whip into long, curved tails as is shown in the painting.

A Binary Star

A s a cloud of dust and gas contracts, it gets warm, especially at its center. Whenever gas is compressed it warms up, and a contracting cloud is being compressed, especially at its center. What's more, as the cloud compresses, the molecules and particles within it hit each other and coalesce, and the energy of their motion is converted into heat.

The heat at the center increases until temperatures in the millions of degrees are reached. At such high temperatures, the atoms and molecules are broken up and the tiny nuclei at the very center of the atoms are stripped of their protective electron shells. The nuclei themselves smash together and undergo "fusion" into larger nuclei. In particular, hydrogen nuclei (the most common) fuse into helium.

This fusion produces still more heat, great quantities of it, so that the entire contracting cloud begins to glow and radiate light and heat. In other words, the contracting cloud ignites and becomes a star.

If the cloud is pretty evenly dense to begin with, it may contract about a single core, and ignite only in one place and thus produce a single star. Our Sun, for instance, is a single star.

If the cloud is not even in density, it may start condensing about two or more cores. Eventually two stars may form that are closer to each other than stars generally are. Trapped in each other's gravity, the two stars circle each other as a "binary star." Perhaps half of all the stars are actually binary systems. If they are far enough apart, each star in the binary can have planets of its own. A person on the planet of such a star, will see his own star as a Sun, and the other as merely a very bright star. If the two stars of a binary are very close, each is deformed by the gravitational pull of the other into an oval, with matter from the smaller pulled out in streamers. The painting shows the view from a planet of such a binary.

The Crab Nebula

*J*ust as a star is born, it must some day die. What makes a star shine and radiate light and heat and keep itself inflated against the steady pull of its own gravity is its capacity to turn hydrogen into helium by nuclear fusion. But a star only has so much hydrogen.

Each star will some day run out of its hydrogen supply. As the core swells with more and more helium, that core grows denser and denser, and hotter and hotter. Finally, the core becomes dense enough and hot enough for helium nuclei to begin fusing to still more complicated nuclei. The whole star heats up and expands into a giant. As it heats up, the gas on the surface cools down to a mere red-heat. The star is then a "red giant."

The energy available through the fusion of helium and other complicated nuclei doesn't last long. In the most massive stars, there is then nothing to keep the star inflated against gravity—so it collapses. When it collapses, the matter from the star's outer regions bounces outward and a great deal of energy is released.

The more massive a star, the more quickly the core hydrogen is consumed—the vaster the red giant that is formed—the more forceful the collapse—the more rapidly the remaining hydrogen is fused—the more violent the final energy-release is.

A very large star can explode as a "supernova." Over a few days, it can turn out energy at the rate of a hundred billion times that of our Sun.

In 1054, a supernova blazed out 5,000 light-years away from us and for a few weeks shone more brightly than Venus. Now, in the place of that exploding star, we see a mass of hot, tortured gases, still expanding. The ball of gas is called, from its appearance, the Crab Nebula, and it is shown in the painting.

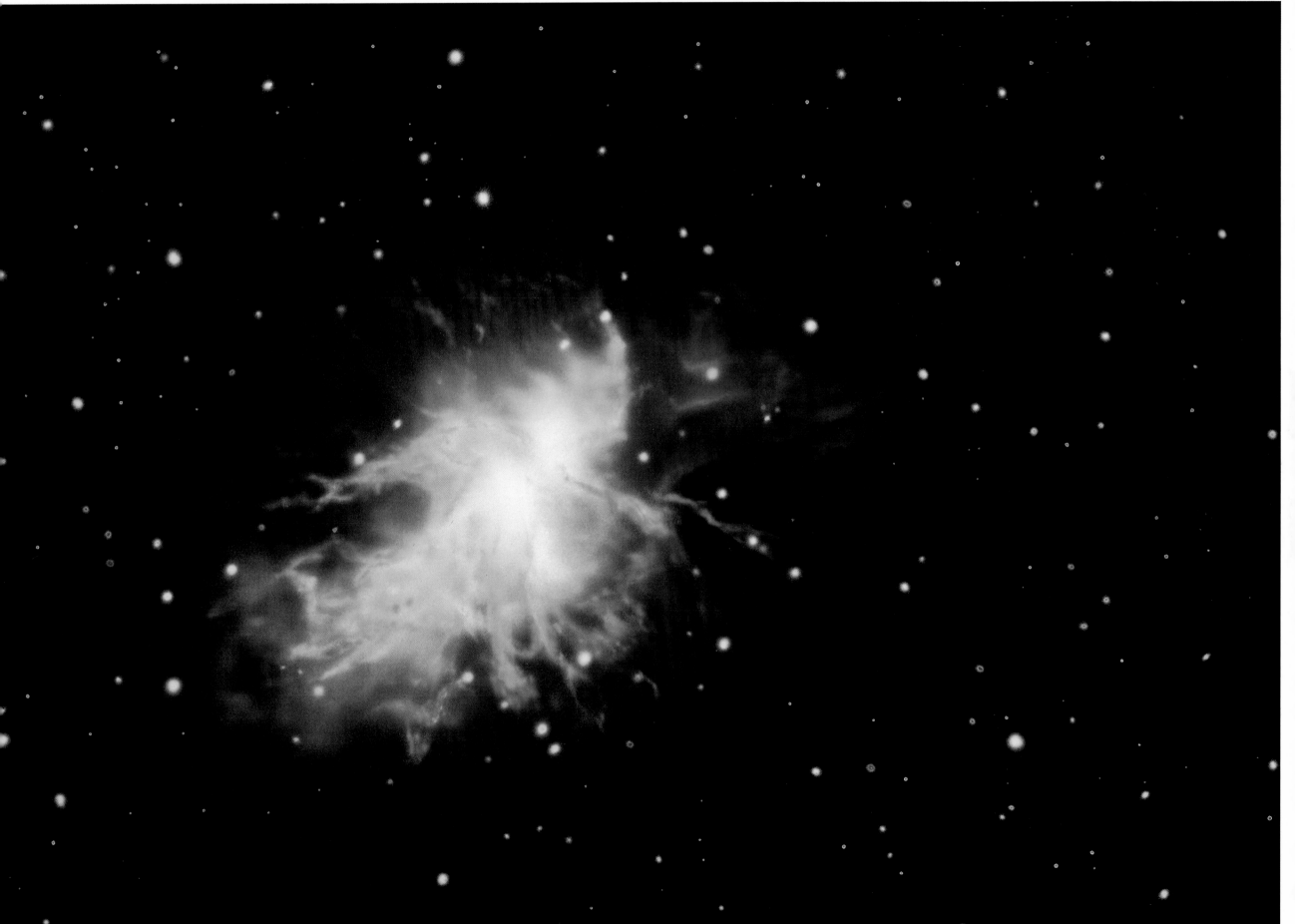

Black Hole

What happens to a star that has used up its fuel and no longer has the energy to keep itself expanded against the pull of its own gravity? Stars with much more mass than the Sun contract into small, dense objects. The more massive the original star, the smaller and denser the final object.

A star like our Sun will never collapse altogether but will slowly shrink instead to the size of a small planet. The Sun's atoms will break up and it will consist of a mixture of bare nuclei and bare electrons. It will be a "white dwarf."

The collapsing portion of a massive star that becomes a supernova is so massive that in its vigorous contraction, its electrons are driven into the nuclei. The protons within the nuclei would be neutralized by the electrons and all that would be left would be uncharged neutrons in virtual contact.

We would then have a "neutron star" only ten to fifteen kilometers across. It would be no larger than a small asteroid but it would have all the mass of a star squeezed into its small volume. It would be enormously dense and it would have an extremely intense gravitational field on its surface.

The collapse might be so massive and sudden that even the neutrons would not withstand the increasingly intense gravitational field. The neutrons would merge and all the mass of a star would move inward toward zero volume and infinite density. So great would the gravitational intensity become that nothing could escape. Objects falling in would not emerge. It would be as though they had fallen into a hole in space. Even light could not emerge, so it would be a "black hole."

Suppose one of the members of a binary star formed a black hole. It could not be seen, but matter from the still normal partner could be attracted into the black hole (as shown in the painting) releasing X-rays in the process. In some places in the heavens, astronomers suspect they are detecting such X-rays.

Iwasaki 1006

The Milky Way

S uppose, though, that we look out at *all* the starry sky. It does not look the same in all directions because, as we now know, the stars nearest ourselves are collected into a large, flat, round system, something like a Frisbee.

If we look at the sky in the directions more or less at right angles to the long diameter of the system, our line of sight soon reaches beyond its thickness into the blackness beyond. If we look at the sky along the long diameter, we see an endless mass of stars that fade into a foggily luminous band across the sky, and that is the Milky Way.

We are quite far toward one end of the system. If we look longways toward the near end, we should see far fewer stars than if we look in the opposite direction toward the center of the system and then beyond that to the far end. We would expect the Milky Way would be fainter on one side and far brighter on the opposite side.

That's not so, however, for the Milky Way is more or less equally bright all the way around. That is because dark clouds of gas in the Milky Way cut off the more distant reaches.

But not entirely. The center of the Galaxy is located in the constellation Sagittarius and there it *is* rather brighter than anywhere else. It is richer in stars and star clusters, for one-third of all the globular clusters in the sky (each containing at least tens of thousands of stars) are located in that constellation.

In the painting, we see that portion of the Milky Way as it would look if we were viewing it from clear space. You can see the dark clouds of non-luminous gas that block off the still brighter and more crowded regions beyond. Fortunately, we can now penetrate those clouds with radio waves, and we have learned something of what goes on at the center. At the very center, there is a great deal of activity and radiation. There may be a giant black hole there.

Kazuaki Iwasaki 007

The Galaxy

*N*ow let us imagine ourselves so far away from our starting point, that we have travelled hundreds of thousands of light-years and are outside our star system altogether and can look back and see it as a whole. We would see it as a structure we call the Galaxy (from Greek words meaning "milky way").

If we saw the Galaxy, as a whole, from outside, we would find it an enormous flat structure not so much like a Frisbee as like a pin-wheel. It is 100,000 light years across and contains up to 400 billion stars, most of them smaller than our Sun. Perhaps nine-tenths of all stars are to be found in the central regions of the Galaxy which blazes with light in the painting. (The painting shows us the Galaxy seen neither face-on, nor edge-on, but obliquely.)

Tens of billions of stars are more thinly spread out in the long spiral arms that stretch out and around from the Galactic core. From a distance, the spiral arms would seem to be like coiling lines of fog, but about the edges the dim flicker of individual stars might be seen. The brighter objects that show in the painting above and below the core, are not stars, but are globular clusters, each one a densely-packed mass of anywhere from 10,000 to 1,000,000 stars.

And where is our Sun located? Not in the Galactic core, you may be sure. If it were, our night sky would be alive with millions of visible stars, and of these many thousands would be brighter than any we see. But we need not regret the lack of that. The core is a violent radiation-filled place and life is probably impossible there.

Our Sun is in one of the spiral arms, 30,000 light-years from the center of the Galaxy. It means that our night-sky is dull, but it is quiet and safe out here. The sun makes a slow circle around the Galactic core, completing one turn in about 240,000,000 years.

The Birth of the Solar System

Our Galaxy is not all there is to the Universe. Beyond our Galaxy are other star-systems, some larger than our Galaxy, most smaller, and possibly as many as a hundred billion of them altogether.

But we have moved outward far enough in our journey. We began at the surface of the Sun and moved outward so far that we could see our entire Galaxy. Now let us, in a way, retrace our steps and return to our beginning. If we start with our Galaxy (formed twelve billion years ago or more) let us see how our Sun was formed, and all its planets.

The painting shows our Galaxy in the upper left and in the spiral arms you can see that a supernova has exploded.

To the right of the Galaxy, we see an expanded view of the supernova which is expanding toward the cloud of dust and gas to *its* right. You see that cloud faintly—it is the raw material of our Solar system.

The explosive force of the supernova sets up a wave of contraction in the cloud and sets up a cycle of contraction within it. The cloud contracts and shrinks in size, at the same time speeding its rotation in accordance with the law of conservation of angular momentum. The cloud flattens out into a disc, with minor remnants stretching out in the equatorial plane of the major mass in the center—as you can see in the extreme upper right of the painting.

As you follow the clockwise curve in the painting, you see the interior portion of the cloud become a star once fusion at its core ignites.

In the outskirts the debris collects into larger bodies, which sweep up the smaller bodies in their path as they circle the Sun—thus becoming still larger and forming the planets. On the smaller planets and on the satellites which are mostly airless, the final impacts leave craters as their mark.

At the lower left you see the young Sun, with its innermost planets: Mercury, Venus, and, nearest us, Earth. It all happened 4,600,000,000 years ago.